CGP

GCSE English Literature AQA Anthology

Conflict

The Workbook
Higher Level

This book will help you prepare for the Anthology
part of your GCSE English Literature exam.

It contains lots of questions designed to make you an
expert on writing about poetry.

It's ideal for use as a homework book or to help you revise.

What CGP is all about

Our sole aim here at CGP is to produce the highest quality
books — carefully written, immaculately presented and
dangerously close to being funny.

Then we work our socks off to get them out to you
— at the cheapest possible prices.

CONTENTS

Section One — Poems from the Literary Heritage

Section Two — Contemporary Poems

Section Three — Themes

Section Four — Analysing Answers

Published by Coordination Group Publications Ltd.

Editors:
Edward Robinson, Hayley Thompson, Emma Warhurst

Produced with:
Alison Smith, Peter Thomas, Nicola Woodfin

Contributors:
Alison Smith, Kevin Smith

With thanks to Luke von Kotze and Nicola Woodfin for the proofreading
and Jan Greenway for copyright research.

ISBN: 978 1 84762 527 4
Groovy website: www.cgpbooks.co.uk
Jolly bits of clipart from CorelDRAW®
Printed by Elanders Hindson Ltd, Newcastle upon Tyne

Based on the classic CGP style created by Richard Parsons.

How to Use this Book

This book is for anyone studying the <u>Conflict</u> cluster of the AQA GCSE English Literature <u>Poetry Anthology</u>. It's got loads of <u>questions</u> in it to help you get your head around the poems.

Sections One and Two are About the Poems

There's a double page on each poem. It looks a bit like this:

There's some info about the <u>poet</u> here.

There's plenty of <u>space</u> around the poem for you to make <u>notes</u>.

Difficult words are defined in the <u>Poem Dictionary</u>.

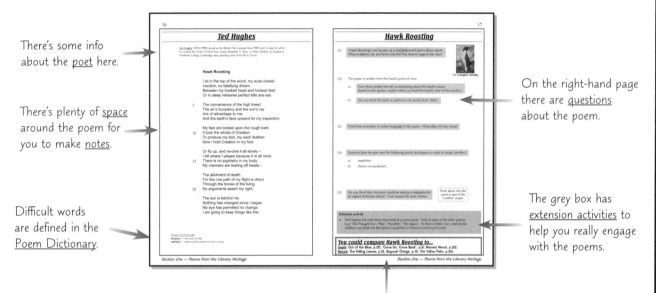

On the right-hand page there are <u>questions</u> about the poem.

The grey box has <u>extension activities</u> to help you really engage with the poems.

The top tip box lists some of the <u>other</u> poems in the cluster with <u>similar themes</u>.

A little bit about the questions...

This is the most important bit...

1) The questions are designed to get you <u>thinking for yourself</u> about the poem.

2) They start off nice and <u>simple</u>, then get <u>trickier</u> as you go down the page.

3) Answer the questions as <u>thoroughly</u> as you can.
   It's important to get to know the poems <u>inside out</u>.

4) Answers can be found in the <u>separate Answer Book</u>.

The questions in these two sections mostly ask you about <u>technical</u> stuff like <u>language</u>, <u>structure</u> and <u>form</u>.

How to Use this Book

Comparing the poems is one of the most important things you'll have to do — that's what Section Three is all about. The questions in it will help you link the different poems by their themes.

Section Three is About the Themes

A double-page spread in the Themes section looks a bit like this:

A different theme is covered on each page.

There are questions about the theme and how different poems relate to it.

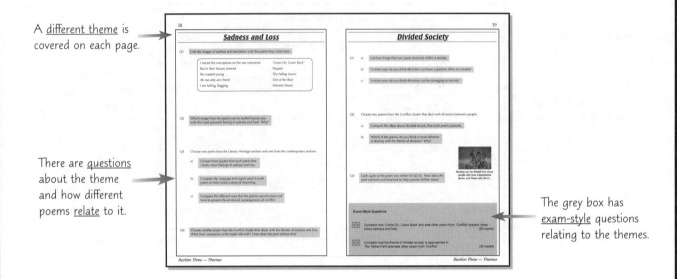

The grey box has exam-style questions relating to the themes.

This is a Really Useful Section

1) The questions are designed to get you thinking about the poems' themes and ideas.

2) They'll also get you to compare the poems — which is just what you'll need to do to get good marks in your exam.

3) The exam-style questions are exactly that — questions like the ones you'll get in your exam. Use them to practise planning and writing answers. Trust me, it'll really help when it comes to the real thing.

Remember: the themes covered in this section aren't the only ones you can write about — they're here to give you some ideas. Once you start thinking about the poems and comparing them with each other, you're bound to come up with a few more of your own.

How to Use this Book

One of the <u>best ways</u> to learn what gets you marks is to <u>analyse</u> some <u>exam-style answers</u>. So that's what you'll be doing in Section Four. You <u>lucky thing</u>, you.

Section Four lets you Analyse some Answers

A page in Section Four looks a bit like this:

These instructions tell you what you have to do (more on this below).

There's an exam-style question at the top of the page.

This is a sample extract from a student's answer.

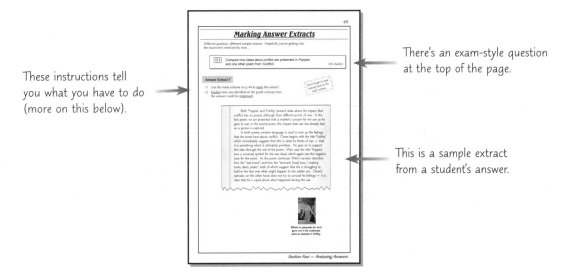

This Section Helps You Understand How to Do Well

1) Most of the questions in this section ask you to <u>grade</u> a <u>sample exam answer</u>.

2) They'll also ask you to say what the answer needs to do to <u>score more marks</u> — this will help you understand how to <u>improve</u> your own answers.

3) Some of the questions ask you to <u>extend a point</u> or <u>give a quote</u> from the poem to back a point up. This helps you to understand how to really <u>use the poems</u> to write a top-notch answer.

<u>Remember</u>: there's <u>more than one right answer</u> to the questions that you'll get in your poetry exam. These sample answers are just designed to show you the <u>kinds of points</u> you'll need to make and the <u>kind of writing style</u> you'll need to use to get a top grade.

Wilfred Owen

Wilfred Owen (1893-1918) was born in Shropshire to an English and Welsh family and was best
known for his war poems written whilst he served in the trenches in World War One.
He died in battle only one week before the end of the war.

Futility

Move him into the sun –
Gently its touch awoke him once,
At home, whispering of fields half-sown.
Always it woke him, even in France,
5   Until this morning and this snow.
If anything might rouse him now
The kind old sun will know.

Think how it wakes the seeds –
Woke once the clays of a cold star.
10   Are limbs, so dear achieved, are sides,
Full-nerved, still warm, too hard to stir?
Was it for this the clay grew tall?
– O what made fatuous sunbeams toil
To break earth's sleep at all?

I'm not fatuous —
this jumper's just a
bit unflattering.

POEM DICTIONARY
fatuous — unthinkingly foolish

Futility

Q1   Wilfred Owen's poem is about a wartime tragedy.

   a)   Explain how the mood of the poem is established from the beginning.

   b)   What is the key difference between the first and second stanzas?

Q2   How could 'Futility' be described as "almost a sonnet, but not quite"?

Think about the number of lines, the subject and the use of rhymes.

Q3   Give examples of how the poet uses personification in the first stanza. What is its effect?

Q4   Why do you think Owen uses the adjective "fatuous" in line 13?

Q5   How does the poet present his ideas about the following themes:

   a)   the consequences of conflict   b)   comradeship

Q6   Why do you think Wilfred Owen chose the title 'Futility' for this poem?

Extension activities
- Read some other poems by Wilfred Owen. How does this poem compare to them?
- Find out about the conditions of trench warfare during World War I (1914-1918). Why do you think this war inspired so many poets?

Other poems with similar themes...
Effects of conflict: The Charge of the Light Brigade, p.6, Bayonet Charge, p.10;
Sadness and loss: The Falling Leaves, p.12, 'Come On, Come Back', p.8, Poppies, p.32.

Alfred Tennyson

<u>Alfred Tennyson</u> (1809-1892) was born in Lincolnshire and later lived on the Isle of Wight and in Surrey. He studied at Trinity College, Cambridge. Tennyson was one of the great poets of the Victorian era and was Poet Laureate from 1850 to 1892.

The Charge of the Light Brigade

1.
Half a league, half a league,
Half a league onward,
All in the valley of Death
    Rode the six hundred.
5 'Forward, the Light Brigade!
Charge for the guns!' he said:
Into the valley of Death
    Rode the six hundred.

2.
    'Forward, the Light Brigade!'
10 Was there a man dismay'd?
Not tho' the soldier knew
    Some one had blunder'd:
Theirs not to make reply,
Theirs not to reason why,
15 Theirs but to do and die:
Into the valley of Death
    Rode the six hundred.

3.
Cannon to right of them,
Cannon to left of them,
20 Cannon in front of them
    Volley'd and thunder'd;
Storm'd at with shot and shell,
Boldly they rode and well,
Into the jaws of Death,
25 Into the mouth of Hell
    Rode the six hundred.

4.
Flash'd all their sabres bare,
Flash'd as they turn'd in air
Sabring the gunners there,
30 Charging an army, while
    All the world wonder'd:
Plunged in the battery-smoke
Right thro' the line they broke;
Cossack and Russian
35 Reel'd from the sabre stroke
    Shatter'd and sunder'd.
Then they rode back, but not
    Not the six hundred.

5.
Cannon to right of them,
40 Cannon to left of them,
Cannon behind them
    Volley'd and thunder'd;
Storm'd at with shot and shell,
While horse and hero fell,
45 They that had fought so well
Came thro' the jaws of Death
Back from the mouth of Hell,
All that was left of them,
    Left of six hundred.

6.
50 When can their glory fade?
O the wild charge they made!
    All the world wonder'd.
Honour the charge they made!
Honour the Light Brigade,
55   Noble six hundred!

<u>POEM DICTIONARY</u>
sabre — a curved sword often used by cavalry soldiers
sunder'd — violently broken apart

The Charge of the Light Brigade

Q1   The poem is about an incident that took place during the Crimean War.

   How does the poet set the scene for the poem in the first four lines?

Q2   Explain the importance of the following in the poem:

   a)   rhythm   b)   repetition

Q3   Find a quote from the poem that highlights each of the themes shown below.
      Copy and complete the table to explain your choices.

Theme	Quote	Explanation
Obedience	"Theirs but to do and die"	They didn't question the order to charge.
Patriotism		
Sacrifice		
Heroism		
The romance of conflict		

Q4   What does the poem suggest about Tennyson's attitude towards the commanding officers who gave the order to charge?

Harry was secretly relieved that his horse hadn't learnt how to charge yet.

Q5   What impression do you think the poet is trying to give in the final stanza of the poem? How does he do this?

Extension activities

• Find out as much as you can about the Crimean War. Do the descriptions in the poem match the information you've found?

• Tennyson was Poet Laureate when he wrote this poem. Find out what a 'Poet Laureate' is and say whether you think this tells us anything about the poem.

You could compare this poem to...

Patriotism: next to of course god america i, p.14, Flag, p.18; Reality of conflict: Bayonet Charge, p.10, Belfast Confetti, p.30; Effects of conflict: Futility, p.4, Poppies, p.32.

Stevie Smith

Weeping bitterly for her ominous mind, her plight,
Up the river of white moonlight she swims
30   Until a treacherous undercurrent
Seizing her in an icy-amorous embrace
Dives with her, swiftly severing
The waters which close above her head.

An enemy sentinel
35   Finding the abandoned clothes
Waits for the swimmer's return
('Come on, come back')
Waiting, whiling away the hour
Whittling a shepherd's pipe from the hollow reeds.
40   In the chill light of dawn
Ring out the pipe's wild notes
'Come on, come back'.

Vaudevue
In the swift and subtle current's close embrace
45   Sleeps on, stirs not, hears not the familiar tune
Favourite of all the troops of all the armies
Favourite of Vaudevue
For she had sung it too
Marching to Austerlitz,
50   'Come on, come back'.

POEM DICTIONARY
Austerlitz — the scene of a battle in the Napoleonic Wars in 1805
hummock — a little hill
Memel — a real town in Nazi Germany, now in Lithuania
M.L.5 — an imaginary poisonous gas
ominous — suggesting that something bad is going to happen

The team celebrated
winning the league with an
icy-amorous embrace.

Stevie Smith

Stevie Smith (1902-1971), real name 'Florence', was born in Kingston upon Hull, but spent most of her life living in North London with her aunt, working for Newnes Publishing Company. She was awarded the Queen's Gold Medal for Poetry in 1969.

'Come On, Come Back'

Incident in a future war

Left by the ebbing tide of battle
On the field of Austerlitz
The girl soldier Vaudevue sits
Her fingers tap the ground, she is alone
5   At midnight in the moonlight she is sitting alone on a round flat stone.

Graded by the Memel Conference first
Of all human exterminators
M.L.5.
Has left her just alive
10   Only her memory is dead for evermore.
She fears and cries, Ah me why am I here?
Sitting alone on a round flat stone on a hummock there.

Rising, staggering, over the ground she goes
Over the seeming miles of rutted meadow
15   To the margin of a lake
The sand beneath her feet
Is cold and damp and firm to the waves' beat.

Quickly – as a child, an idiot, as one without memory –
She strips her uniform off, strips, stands and plunges
20   Into the icy waters of the adorable lake.
On the surface of the water lies
A ribbon of white moonlight
The waters on either side of the moony track
Are black as her mind,
25   Her mind is as secret from her
As the water on which she swims,
As secret as profound as ominous.

THIS IS A FLAP.
FOLD THIS PAGE OUT.

'Come On, Come Back'

Q1 The poem's subtitle is 'Incident in a future war'.

    a)   What features of the poem fit in with this subtitle?

    b)   Describe how the first stanza sets the scene for the rest of the poem.

Q2 Explain the role of the following poetic techniques in creating the poem's mood:

    a)   rhyme

    b)   repetition

    c)   alliteration

Q3   a)   Do you think 'Come On, Come Back' is a good name for the poem? Why?

    b)   What do you think would be a good alternative title for the poem and why?

Q4 What impression do you get of the enemy sentinel playing his pipe?
Give reasons for your ideas.

Q5 What do you think is the significance of the lake?
Think about the poet's descriptions of it and what they suggest.

Extension activity

- 'Come On, Come Back' could be described as a science fiction poem. What is science fiction? Find some other works of science fiction (e.g. short stories, poems) that contain warnings about the future, and compare them to 'Come On, Come Back'.

Other poems that deal with similar issues...

<u>Sadness and loss</u>: Poppies, p.32, The Falling Leaves, p.12, Futility, p.4, Mametz Wood, p.22;
<u>Individual experiences</u>: Out of the Blue, p.20, The Right Word, p.26, At the Border, 1979, p.28.

Ted Hughes

Ted Hughes (1930-1998) served as the British Poet Laureate from 1984 until he died, for which he received the Order of Merit from Queen Elizabeth II. Born in West Yorkshire, he studied at Pembroke College, Cambridge, later spending most of his life in Devon.

Bayonet Charge

Suddenly he awoke and was running – raw
In raw-seamed hot khaki, his sweat heavy,
Stumbling across a field of clods towards a green hedge
That dazzled with rifle fire, hearing
5   Bullets smacking the belly out of the air –
He lugged a rifle numb as a smashed arm:
The patriotic tear that had brimmed in his eye
Sweating like molten iron from the centre of his chest –

In bewilderment then he almost stopped –
10   In what cold clockwork of the stars and the nations
Was he the hand pointing that second? He was running
Like a man who has jumped up in the dark and runs
Listening between his footfalls for the reason
Of his still running, and his foot hung like
15   Statuary in mid-stride. Then the shot-slashed furrows

Threw up a yellow hare that rolled like a flame
And crawled in a threshing circle, its mouth wide
Open silent, its eyes standing out.
He plunged past with his bayonet toward the green hedge.
20   King, honour, human dignity, etcetera
Dropped like luxuries in a yelling alarm
To get out of that blue crackling air
His terror's touchy dynamite.

Once again, Andrew won the point
with a mid-stride net charge.

Bayonet Charge

Q1   How does the beginning of the poem create a strong impression of the horror of battle?

Q2   The poem is divided into three stanzas of eight, seven and eight lines.

How do you think the different ideas in the three stanzas contrast with each other? What is the effect of this structure?

Q3   Describe the effect of the enjambment between the second and third stanzas.

Q4   Find three examples of imagery in the first stanza of the poem.

a)   Explain the impact of each image.

b)   Which image do you think is the most effective? Why?

Q5   What do you think the following quotes mean, and why are they effective?

a)   "In what cold clockwork of the stars and the nations / Was he the hand pointing that second?"

b)   "King, honour, human dignity, etcetera / Dropped like luxuries in a yelling alarm".

Q6   Explain why you think the "yellow hare" is included in the third stanza, and what its behaviour means.

> Think about how the description of the hare links with the soldier's situation.

Extension activity

*   Sketch out a storyboard with three or four frames, showing the main incidents described in the poem. Use a quote from the poem to annotate each frame.

Other poems in the Conflict cluster with similar themes...

Effects of conflict: Futility, p.4, The Charge of the Light Brigade, p.6; Reality of conflict: Belfast Confetti, p.30; Nature: Hawk Roosting, p.16, Mametz Wood, p.22, The Falling Leaves, p.12.

Margaret Postgate Cole

Dame Margaret Postgate Cole (1893-1980) was an English politician and writer who campaigned against conscription during the First World War. She studied at Cambridge and worked as a teacher whilst writing, before entering politics in 1941 specialising in education.

The Falling Leaves

November 1915

Today, as I rode by,
I saw the brown leaves dropping from their tree
In a still afternoon,
When no wind whirled them whistling to the sky,
5   But thickly, silently,
They fell, like snowflakes wiping out the noon;
And wandered slowly thence
For thinking of a gallant multitude
Which now all withering lay,
10   Slain by no wind of age or pestilence,
But in their beauty strewed
Like snowflakes falling on the Flemish clay.

POEM DICTIONARY
slain — killed deliberately

The Falling Leaves

Q1   What did you expect the poem to be about from the title?
Does the content fit with what you expected?

This poem is about *so* much
more than a few falling leaves.

Q2   How does the poet use natural imagery in the poem?

Q3   Look at line 8 of the poem.

a)   How did the "gallant multitude" die?

b)   What can you tell about how the narrator feels about them?

Q4   Explain how the following affect the meaning of the poem:

a)   form and structure

b)   rhyme

c)   alliteration

Q5   Look at the last two lines of the poem.

a)   What do you think these lines mean?

b)   What impression are you left with at the end of the poem?

Extension activity

- This poem was written in 1915. Look at some poems, stories, books or films produced during the First World War. How do you think they reflected and influenced attitudes towards war in this period?

You could compare The Falling Leaves to...

Nature: Hawk Roosting, p.16, Mametz Wood, p.22, Bayonet Charge, p.10; Sadness and loss: Futility, p.4, 'Come On, Come Back', p.8, Poppies, p.32; Helplessness: Out of the Blue, p.20.

E E Cummings

Edward Estlin Cummings (1894-1962) was an American poet, born in Massachusetts, who studied at Harvard University and later travelled within Europe and North Africa throughout the 1920s and 1930s.

next to of course god america i

"next to of course god america i
love you land of the pilgrims' and so forth oh
say can you see by the dawn's early my
country 'tis of centuries come and go
5 and are no more what of it we should worry
in every language even deafanddumb
thy sons acclaim your glorious name by gorry
by jingo by gee by gosh by gum
why talk of beauty what could be more beaut-
10 iful than these heroic happy dead
who rushed like lions to the roaring slaughter
they did not stop to think they died instead
then shall the voice of liberty be mute?"

He spoke. And drank rapidly a glass of water

What was that rule
again... something about
starting sentences...
nope, can't remember.

next to of course god america i

Q1   'next to of course god america i' could appear to be a patriotic poem.

    a)   What might cause the reader to get this impression?

    b)   What clues are there in the poem that this isn't actually the case?

Q2   Explain what you think the following quotes mean, and why they are effective.

    a)   "thy sons acclaim your glorious name by gorry / by jingo by gee by gosh by gum"
    b)   "what of it we should worry"

Q3   Examine how the poet presents his ideas on the following:

    a)   time
    b)   patriotism
    c)   the power of language

Q4   How do the form and structure of this poem influence our understanding of its message?

Q5   Is it possible to get a positive message from this poem? Give reasons for your answer.

Extension activity

- Find out what "jingoism" means. Do you think jingoism exists today?
  Give reasons for your answer.

- Compare 'next to of course god america i' to some other poems by E E Cummings.
  Do they express similar views?

Other poems in the Conflict cluster have similar themes...
Patriotism: The Charge of the Light Brigade, p.6, Flag, p.18, 'Come On, Come Back', p.8;
Causes of conflict: The Yellow Palm, p.24, Hawk Roosting, p.16, The Right Word, p.26.

Ted Hughes

Ted Hughes (1930-1998) served as the British Poet Laureate from 1984 until he died, for which he received the Order of Merit from Queen Elizabeth II. Born in West Yorkshire, he studied at Pembroke College, Cambridge, later spending most of his life in Devon.

Hawk Roosting

I sit in the top of the wood, my eyes closed.
Inaction, no falsifying dream
Between my hooked head and hooked feet:
Or in sleep rehearse perfect kills and eat.

5   The convenience of the high trees!
The air's buoyancy and the sun's ray
Are of advantage to me;
And the earth's face upward for my inspection.

My feet are locked upon the rough bark.
10   It took the whole of Creation
To produce my foot, my each feather:
Now I hold Creation in my foot

Or fly up, and revolve it all slowly –
I kill where I please because it is all mine.
15   There is no sophistry in my body:
My manners are tearing off heads –

The allotment of death.
For the one path of my flight is direct
Through the bones of the living.
20   No arguments assert my right:

The sun is behind me.
Nothing has changed since I began.
My eye has permitted no change.
I am going to keep things like this.

POEM DICTIONARY
buoyancy — the power to float
sophistry — reasoning that sounds true but is wrong

Hawk Roosting

Q1   'Hawk Roosting' may be seen as a straightforward poem about nature. What evidence can you find in the first five lines to support this idea?

I'm a penguin, actually.

Q2   The poem is written from the hawk's point of view.

   a)   Give three quotes that tell us something about the hawk's nature. Based on the quotes, explain what you think the hawk's view of the world is.

   b)   Do you think the hawk is justified in its world view? Why?

Q3   Find three examples of violent language in the poem. What effect do they have?

Q4   Examine how the poet uses the following poetic techniques in order to create an effect:

   a)   repetition

   b)   choice of vocabulary

Q5   Do you think that this poem could be read as a metaphor for an aspect of human nature? Give reasons for your answer.

> Think about why this poem is part of the 'Conflict' cluster.

Extension activity

- Ted Hughes has often been described as a nature poet. Look at some of his other poems (e.g. 'The Thought-Fox', 'Pike', 'Thrushes', 'The Jaguar', 'To Paint a Water Lily') and decide whether you think the description is justified or if there is more to his work.

You could compare Hawk Roosting to...

<u>Death</u>: Out of the Blue, p.20, 'Come On, Come Back', p.8, Mametz Wood, p.22;
<u>Nature</u>: The Falling Leaves, p.12, Bayonet Charge, p.10, The Yellow Palm, p.24.

John Agard

John Agard was born in Guyana in South America in 1949 and moved to Britain in 1977. He likes to perform his poems, and believes humour is an effective way of challenging people's opinions.

Flag

What's that fluttering in a breeze?
It's just a piece of cloth
that brings a nation to its knees.

What's that unfurling from a pole?
5   It's just a piece of cloth
that makes the guts of men grow bold.

What's that rising over a tent?
It's just a piece of cloth
that dares the coward to relent.

10   What's that flying across a field?
It's just a piece of cloth
that will outlive the blood you bleed.

How can I possess such a cloth?
Just ask for a flag, my friend.
15   Then blind your conscience to the end.

Flag

Q1   How is the mood of the poem established in the first stanza?

Q2   Why do you think the poet uses a rhetorical question at the beginning of each stanza?

Q3   The flag is repeatedly described as "just a piece of cloth".

    a)   How is this description contradicted in the poem?

    b)   What do you think the poet is trying to show with this contradiction?

Q4   Describe how the following contribute to the impact of the poem:

    a)   form

    b)   repetition

    c)   rhyme

It's nice, yes, but can it make
the guts of men grow bold?

Q5   What do you think is the message of the final stanza?

Extension activity

• Choose three different national flags and find out what each flag shows and symbolises.

• Investigate some of the ways in which flags have been depicted and used, either:
 a) by the media, b) in art, or c) in politics and protest.

Other poems feature the same themes...

Patriotism: The Charge of the Light Brigade, p.6, next to of course god america i, p.14,
'Come On, Come Back', p.8; Causes of conflict: The Yellow Palm, p.24, The Right Word, p.26.

Simon Armitage

Simon Armitage was born in 1963 in West Yorkshire. As well as poetry, he's also written four stage plays, and writes for TV, film and radio. He now teaches creative writing at Manchester Metropolitan University.

Extract from **Out of the Blue**

You have picked me out.
Through a distant shot of a building burning
you have noticed now
that a white cotton shirt is twirling, turning.

5   In fact I am waving, waving.
Small in the clouds, but waving, waving.
Does anyone see
a soul worth saving?

So when will you come?
10   Do you think you are watching, watching
a man shaking crumbs
or pegging out washing?

I am trying and trying.
The heat behind me is bullying, driving,
15   but the white of surrender is not yet flying.
I am not at the point of leaving, diving.

A bird goes by.
The depth is appalling. Appalling
that others like me
20   should be wind-milling, wheeling, spiralling, falling.

Are your eyes believing,
believing
that here in the gills
I am still breathing.

25   But tiring, tiring.
Sirens below are wailing, firing.
My arm is numb and my nerves are sagging.
Do you see me, my love. I am failing, flagging.

Out of the Blue

Q1   The poem is about the September 11th terrorist attack on the World Trade Centre in New York.

a)   Who is narrating the poem? How do you know?

b)   Who does the narrator seem to be directing the poem at?

Q2   How does the narrator's attitude towards his situation change through the course of the poem?

Q3   Explain how the following contribute to the poem's mood:

a)   repetition

b)   rhyme

c)   alliteration

Q4   What is the effect of the image of the bird in the fifth stanza?

Q5   How do the poem's form and structure contribute to its overall impact?

Extension activity

• Research the terrorist attack on the World Trade Centre which this poem is about.
  How were ordinary people affected by the attack?

Other poems with similar themes...

Owen Sheers

Owen Sheers was born in 1974 in Fiji but grew up in Abergavenny in South Wales. As well as poetry, he has worked in theatre and television, and was Writer in Residence for The Wordsworth Trust in 2004.

Mametz Wood

For years afterwards the farmers found them –
the wasted young, turning up under their plough blades
as they tended the land back into itself.

A chit of bone, the china plate of a shoulder blade,
5   the relic of a finger, the blown
and broken bird's egg of a skull,

all mimicked now in flint, breaking blue in white
across this field where they were told to walk, not run,
towards the wood and its nesting machine guns.

10   And even now the earth stands sentinel,
reaching back into itself for reminders of what happened
like a wound working a foreign body to the surface of the skin.

This morning, twenty men buried in one long grave,
a broken mosaic of bone linked arm in arm,
15   their skeletons paused mid dance-macabre

in boots that outlasted them,
their socketed heads tilted back at an angle
and their jaws, those that have them, dropped open.

As if the notes they had sung
20   have only now, with this unearthing,
slipped from their absent tongues.

If you go down to Mametz
Wood today...

POEM DICTIONARY
Mametz Wood — a real place in the Somme region of France —
the scene of a battle in 1916 where thousands died
dance-macabre — a medieval dance of death

Mametz Wood

Q1   a)   What are the main themes of the poem?

      b)   How are the main themes established in the first stanza?

Q2   Explain the significance of the images in the second stanza.

Q3   Find three examples of imagery from the last four stanzas of the poem.

      a)   Explain why you think the poet chose each image.

      b)   Which image do you think is the most effective? Why?

Q4   Explain how the form and structure of this poem contribute to its meaning.

Look at the significance of the three-line stanzas, and the enjambment between the fifth and sixth stanzas.

Q5   What ideas about life, death and remembrance are presented in the poem?

Extension activity
- Look at Christopher Williams' painting, "The Welsh at Mametz Wood". Does seeing the painting alter your view of the poem?

You should be able to look at the painting online.

Compare Mametz Wood to poems with similar themes...
Death: Out of the Blue, p.20, 'Come On, Come Back', p.8, Hawk Roosting, p.16; Nature: The Falling Leaves, p.12, Bayonet Charge, p.10; Reality of conflict: Belfast Confetti, p.30.

Robert Minhinnick

<u>Robert Minhinnick</u> is a Welsh poet and author, born in Neath in 1952. He studied at
the University of Wales, and has won numerous awards for both his poetry and novels.
He helped to establish two Welsh environmental charities and is an environmental campaigner.

The Yellow Palm

As I made my way down Palestine Street
I watched a funeral pass –
all the women waving lilac stems
around a coffin made of glass
5   and the face of the man who lay within
who had breathed a poison gas.

As I made my way down Palestine Street
I heard the call to prayer
and I stopped at the door of the golden mosque
10   to watch the faithful there
but there was blood on the walls and the muezzin's eyes
were wild with his despair.

As I made my way down Palestine Street
I met two blind beggars
15   And into their hands I pressed my hands
with a hundred black dinars;
and their salutes were those of the Imperial Guard
in the Mother of all Wars.

As I made my way down Palestine Street
20   I smelled the wide Tigris,
the river smell that lifts the air
in a city such as this;
but down on my head fell the barbarian sun
that knows no armistice.

25   As I made my way down Palestine Street
I saw a Cruise missile,
a slow and silver caravan
on its slow and silver mile,
and a beggar child turned up his face
30   and blessed it with a smile.

As I made my way down Palestine Street
under the yellow palms
I saw their branches hung with yellow dates
all sweeter than salaams,
35   and when that same child reached up to touch,
the fruit fell in his arms.

POEM DICTIONARY
Palestine Street — a street
in the centre of Baghdad
muezzin — someone who calls
people to prayer in a mosque
dinar — a unit of currency
Imperial Guard — troops who
guarded Saddam Hussein
Tigris — the river that
runs through Baghdad
Salaam — Islamic greeting
meaning 'peace'

The Yellow Palm

Q1   How does the first stanza establish the mood of the poem?

Q2   The poet describes a series of incidents that take place during a walk through a Middle Eastern city.

        a)   How does this reinforce the poem's atmosphere and message?

        b)   How do the ballad form, repetition, structure and rhyme contribute to the poem's impact?

Q3   How is the reader's understanding and appreciation of each scene affected by the last two lines of each stanza?

Diana had come up with an ingenious way of disguising her yellow palms.

Q4   Copy and fill in the table to show how the poet uses different senses to create a powerful impression. The first one has been done as an example for you.

Sense	Quote	Explanation
Sight	"but there was blood on the walls"	A shocking visual image.
Hearing		
Smell		
Touch		
Taste		

Extension activity

- Look into the setting of the poem. What country is Palestine Street in? What can you find out about the political situation in that country?

Other poems in the Conflict cluster have similar themes...

<u>Causes of conflict:</u> Hawk Roosting, p.16, next to of course god america i, p.14, Flag, p.18;
<u>Divided society:</u> The Right Word, p.26, At the Border, 1979, p.28, Belfast Confetti, p.30.

Imtiaz Dharker

Imtiaz Dharker was born in 1954 in Pakistan. She has said that she believes identity comes from "beliefs and states of mind", rather than nationality or religion.

The Right Word

Outside the door,
lurking in the shadows,
is a terrorist.

Is that the wrong description?
5   Outside that door,
taking shelter in the shadows,
is a freedom-fighter.

I haven't got this right.
Outside, waiting in the shadows,
10 is a hostile militant.

Are words no more
than waving, wavering flags?
Outside your door,
watchful in the shadows,
15 is a guerrilla warrior.

God help me.
Outside, defying every shadow,
stands a martyr.
I saw his face.

20 No words can help me now.
Just outside the door,
lost in shadows,
is a child who looks like mine.

One word for you.
25 Outside my door,
his hand too steady,
his eyes too hard
is a boy who looks like your son, too.

I open the door.
30 Come in, I say.
Come in and eat with us.

The child steps in
and carefully, at my door,
takes off his shoes.

The Right Word

Q1   Copy and complete the table to show the emotional impact that the words used in the poem have on the reader.

Definition	Emotional Impact	Explanation
Terrorist		
Freedom Fighter		
Hostile Militant		
Martyr		
Child		

Q2   The narrator is unhappy with each description she gives of the person outside the door.

a)   Why do you think this is?

b)   How does she deal with this?

The right word for a haircut like this? Hideous.

Q3   a)   How is the poem resolved?

b)   Do you think the resolution is satisfactory? Explain your answer.

Q4   a)   What is the significance of the title of the poem?

b)   Suggest a new title for the poem and explain why you think it would be appropriate.

Q5   Explain how form and structure contribute to the meaning of the poem.

Extension activity

- "War" is an emotive word. List ten words associated with "war" (e.g. "battle", "attack", "army") and explain the different emotional effect that each word has on you. Think about how media usage of these terms affects your attitude.

You could compare The Right Word to...

Divided society: At the Border, 1979, p.28, Belfast Confetti, p.30, The Yellow Palm, p.24;
Individual experiences: Out of the Blue, p.20, Poppies, p.32; Causes of conflict: Flag, p.18.

Choman Hardi

<u>Choman Hardi</u> was born in 1974 in Iraqi Kurdistan, but spent from 1975 to 1979 with her family in Iran. In 1993 she arrived in the UK as a refugee, and went on to study at Oxford, London and Kent Universities. She has published poetry in both Kurdish and English.

At the Border, 1979

'It is your last check-in point in this country!'
We grabbed a drink –
soon everything would taste different.

5   The land under our feet continued
divided by a thick iron chain.

My sister put her leg across it.
'Look over here,' she said to us,
'my right leg is in this country
and my left leg in the other.'
10   The border guards told her off.

Yep, much cleaner.

My mother informed me: *We are going home.*
She said that the roads are much cleaner
the landscape is more beautiful
and people are much kinder.

15   Dozens of families waited in the rain.
'I can inhale home,' somebody said.
Now our mothers were crying. I was five years old
standing by the check-in point
comparing both sides of the border.

20   The autumn soil continued on the other side
with the same colour, the same texture.
It rained on both sides of the chain.

We waited while our papers were checked,
our faces thoroughly inspected.
25   Then the chain was removed to let us through.
A man bent down and kissed his muddy homeland.
The same chain of mountains encompassed all of us.

At the Border, 1979

Q1   a)   Whose point of view is the poem written from?

       b)   Explain how this contributes to the poem's mood and meaning.

Focus on the difference between perception and reality.

Q2   How do the poem's form and structure contribute to its impact?

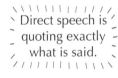

Direct speech is quoting exactly what is said.

Q3   Explain the importance of the use of direct speech in the poem.

Q4   Why do you think the word "chain" is used several times in the poem? Explain your answer.

Q5   What impression does the final stanza leave you with? Why?

Extension activity

•   Imagine how you would feel if you were a refugee. Write a diary entry about your experiences.

Poems that touch on the same issues...

Divided society: The Right Word, p.26, Belfast Confetti, p.30, The Yellow Palm, p.24;
Helplessness: Out of the Blue, p.20, Futility, p.4; Individual experiences: Poppies, p.32.

Ciaran Carson

Ciaran Carson was born in Belfast in 1948. After graduating from the Queen's University in Belfast he worked for the Arts Council of Northern Ireland. He became a Professor at Queen's University in 1998, as well as being Director of the Seamus Heaney Centre for Poetry.

Belfast Confetti

Suddenly as the riot squad moved in it was raining exclamation
    marks,
Nuts, bolts, nails, car-keys. A fount of broken type. And
    the explosion
5   Itself – an asterisk on the map. This hyphenated line, a burst
    of rapid fire...
I was trying to complete a sentence in my head, but it kept
    stuttering,
All the alleyways and side streets blocked with stops and
10   colons.

I know this labyrinth so well – Balaklava, Raglan, Inkerman,
    Odessa Street –
Why can't I escape? Every move is punctuated. Crimea Street.
    Dead end again.
15   A Saracen, Kremlin-2 mesh. Makrolon face-shields. Walkie-
    talkies. What is
My name? Where am I coming from? Where am I going?
    A fusillade of question-marks.

Welsh confetti.

POEM DICTIONARY
Balaklava, Raglan, Inkerman, Odessa Street, Crimea Street — areas and roads in Belfast
(the names are also associated with people and places from the Crimean War)
Saracen — an army vehicle
Kremlin-2 mesh — an anti-rocket mesh fitted to army vehicles
Makrolon — a type of plastic
fusillade — shots fired rapidly one after another

Belfast Confetti

Q1   Explain how the mood of the poem is established in the first sentence.

Q2   a)   What is the central metaphor of the poem?
What impact does it have?

The central metaphor is first mentioned in lines 1-2.

       b)   How does the punctuation in the poem reinforce the central metaphor?

Q3   What effect does it have when the narrator describes the streets as a "labyrinth"?

Q4   Why do you think the poet is so precise in his description of things and places in the second stanza?

Q5   What do you think is the significance of the poem's title?

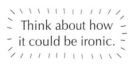

Think about how it could be ironic.

Extension activity

- Find out about the Troubles in Northern Ireland from the 1960s to the 1990s. How and why did they occur and what happened?

Why not compare Belfast Confetti to...

<u>Helplessness</u>: At the Border, 1979, p.28, Out of the Blue, p.20; <u>Reality of battles</u>: The Charge of the Light Brigade, p.6, Bayonet Charge, p.10; <u>Divided society</u>: The Yellow Palm, p.24.

Jane Weir

Jane Weir was born in Salford in 1963 but currently lives and works in Derbyshire. She spent several years in Belfast in Northern Ireland.

Poppies

Three days before Armistice Sunday
and poppies had already been placed
on individual war graves. Before you left,
I pinned one onto your lapel, crimped petals,
5   spasms of paper red, disrupting a blockade
of yellow bias binding around your blazer.

Sellotape bandaged around my hand,
I rounded up as many white cat hairs
as I could, smoothed down your shirt's
10   upturned collar, steeled the softening
of my face. I wanted to graze my nose
across the tip of your nose, play at
being Eskimos like we did when
you were little. I resisted the impulse
15   to run my fingers through the gelled
blackthorns of your hair. All my words
flattened, rolled, turned into felt,

slowly melting. I was brave, as I walked
with you, to the front door, threw
20   it open, the world overflowing
like a treasure chest. A split second
and you were away, intoxicated.
After you'd gone I went into your bedroom,
released a song bird from its cage.
25   Later a single dove flew from the pear tree,
and this is where it has led me,
skirting the church yard walls, my stomach busy
making tucks, darts, pleats, hat-less, without
a winter coat or reinforcements of scarf, gloves.

30   On reaching the top of the hill I traced
the inscriptions on the war memorial,
leaned against it like a wishbone.
The dove pulled freely against the sky,
an ornamental stitch. I listened, hoping to hear
35   your playground voice catching on the wind.

Poppies

Q1   a)   What is the significance of the title of the poem?

I know the poem's called
Poppies, but puppies are
so much cuter.

      b)   Choose an alternative title for the
            poem and explain your choice.

Q2   How is the mood of the poem established in the first three lines?

Q3   a)   Who is the "you" the narrator is referring to?

      b)   Explain how the relationship in the poem is portrayed.

Q4   How does the poet make connections between the past and the present?

Q5   Explain how the form and structure of the poem contribute to its overall effect.

Q6   What do you think is the significance of the songbird and the dove in the poem?

Extension activity
- Using the poem for inspiration, write a description of what you think the son is like.

Other poems with similar themes...
<u>Sadness and loss</u>: Futility, p.4, The Falling Leaves, p.12, 'Come On, Come Back', p.8;
<u>Individual experiences</u>: Out of the Blue, p.20, The Right Word, p.26, At the Border, 1979, p.28.

Conflict — Causes

Q1   a)   Write a list of four different types of conflict.

"How dare you say that about my mother?"

      b)   For each type of conflict, think of something that might have caused it.

Q2   Some of the poems in this cluster deal with the causes of conflict.

      a)   Which of these poems deal with this theme most effectively? Why?

      b)   Which of the poems deal with this theme least effectively? Why?

Q3   Choose two poems from the Conflict cluster and think about what might have motivated the poets to write them. Compare your ideas on the motivation behind each poem.

Q4   Choose two poems from the Conflict cluster and compare the different ways they deal with the causes of conflict. You could look in particular at:

      a)   the different images the poet uses

      b)   emotional impact

      c)   poetic techniques

Conflict — Effects

Q1   List three different types of conflict and then write down the consequences that can come from each of them. You can draw a diagram if you want.

Q2   People can sometimes get involved in conflict and have no control over the consequences.

    a)   Give an example of this from the real world.

    b)   Give an example of this from one of the poems in the Conflict cluster.

Q3   Choose a poem from 'Conflict'.

    a)   Is the poem written in the first or third person?

    b)   How do you think this affects our appreciation of the poem?

Q4   Choose two poems from the Conflict cluster — one from the Literary Heritage section and one from the contemporary section.

    a)   Compare the emotional effects of conflict presented in each poem.

    b)   Find two quotes from each poem that portray the physical effects of conflict effectively. Explain why you chose them.

Exam-Style Questions

Remember to make a proper plan before you start writing your answer.

0 5   Compare how the causes of conflict are presented in *next to of course god america i* and **one** other poem from 'Conflict'.
(36 marks)

0 6   Compare how the effects of conflict are shown in *Out of the Blue* and **one** other poem from 'Conflict'.
(36 marks)

Reality of Battles

Q1   Choose three poems from the Conflict cluster (at least one from the Literary Heritage section and at least one from the contemporary section). Copy the table below and use it to help you complete the following tasks:

a)   Choose two images from each poem that you think vividly convey the reality of battle.

b)   Explain why you have chosen these images.

c)   Which of the poems you have chosen do you think is the most effective at conveying the reality of battle? Why?

	Image 1 and why you chose it	Image 2 and why you chose it
Poem 1		
Poem 2		
Poem 3		

Q2   Compare how the poets in the poems you looked at for Q1 use poetic devices to convey their message.

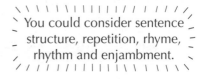

You could consider sentence structure, repetition, rhyme, rhythm and enjambment.

Q3   Choose a poem from the cluster. How accurately do you think it conveys the reality of battle? Explain your answer.

Q4   Which of the poems you have studied do you think has the most emotional impact when describing the reality of battle? Explain your answer.

Nature

Q1   For each of the topics below, choose three poems from 'Conflict'
and describe the role that these topics play in each poem:

a)   Forces of nature (e.g. sun, wind, weather, the land)

b)   Animals and birds

Q2   Which of the poems that you looked at for Q1 do you
think uses natural imagery most effectively? Why?

Q3   Choose a different poem from 'Conflict'.

a)   Which aspects of nature has the poet included in the poem?

b)   Why do you think the poet has used nature in this way?

Q4   Choose a poem from the Conflict cluster that you think deals
with the theme of violence in nature. How does it do this?

Exam-Style Questions

0 5   Compare how the reality of battles is presented in *Bayonet Charge* and
one other poem from 'Conflict'.   *(36 marks)*

0 6   Compare how poets use natural images in *Hawk Roosting* and **one**
other poem from 'Conflict'.   *(36 marks)*

Sadness and Loss

Q1   Link the images of sadness and loss below with the poem they come from.

I traced the inscriptions on the war memorial	'Come On, Come Back'
But in their beauty strewed	Poppies
the wasted young	The Falling Leaves
Ah me why am I here?	Out of the Blue
I am failing, flagging.	Mametz Wood

Q2   Which image from the poems you've studied leaves you with the most powerful feeling of sadness and loss? Why?

Q3   Choose one poem from the Literary Heritage section and one from the contemporary section.

    a)   Choose three quotes from each poem that clearly show feelings of sadness and loss.

    b)   Compare the language techniques used in each poem to help create a sense of mourning.

    c)   Compare the different ways that the poems use structure and form to present the emotional consequences of conflict.

Q4   Choose another poem from the Conflict cluster that deals with the themes of sadness and loss. What final impression is the reader left with? How does the poet achieve this?

Divided Society

Q1   a)   List four things that can cause divisions within a society.

      b)   In what ways do you think divisions can have a positive effect on society?

      c)   In what ways do you think divisions can be damaging to society?

Q2   Choose two poems from the Conflict cluster that deal with divisions between people.

      a)   Compare the ideas about divided society that each poem presents.

      b)   Which of the poems do you think is most effective
            at dealing with the theme of division? Why?

Society can be divided into those
people who love interpretative
dance, and those who don't...

Q3   Look again at the poem you chose for Q2 b). How does the
      poet use form and structure to help convey his/her ideas?

Exam-Style Questions

0 4   Compare how *'Come On, Come Back'* and **one** other poem from 'Conflict' present ideas
       about sadness and loss.   *(36 marks)*

0 5   Compare how the theme of divided society is approached in
       The Yellow Palm and **one** other poem from 'Conflict'.   *(36 marks)*

Patriotism

Q1   Think about the word 'patriotism'.

    a)   What does it mean?

    b)   Do you think that it is a positive or negative force in the world? Why?

Q2   Decide whether each of the statements below is true or false.
Find a quote from the poem to support or disagree with each statement.

In *Bayonet Charge* the soldier loses his patriotic ideals.

E E Cummings approves of unquestioning patriotism.

At the Border, 1979 is a patriotic poem.

In *The Charge of the Light Brigade*, Tennyson praises the soldiers' patriotism.

In *Flag*, John Agard suggests that national flags have too much power.

Q3   Choose two poems that deal with patriotism.

    a)   Compare the ways that the two poems portray patriotism.

    b)   Which of the poems do you think is most successful in getting its message across?

Q4   Choose another poem that has patriotism as one of its themes.

    a)   Does the poem leave you with a positive or negative impression of patriotism?

    b)   What do you think is the overall message of the poem?

Q5   Which of the poems in 'Conflict' do you think contains the most powerful line or phrase regarding patriotism? Give the line or phrase and explain why you think it is so powerful.

Individual Experiences

Q1 Choose two poems that show how conflict can leave people feeling isolated. Explain how the characters are isolated in each poem.

Q2 Which of the poems you looked at for Q1 do you think conveys a sense of isolation most effectively? How does it do this?

Bruce enjoyed the individual experience of solo boules.

Q3 _Poppies_ presents two contrasting individual experiences of the same situation. How do you think this technique reinforces the poem's impact?

Q4 For each of the individual experiences listed below, choose one poem and say how effectively you think the experience is conveyed in the poem.

    a)   confusion

    b)   emotional detachment

    c)   arrogance

Exam-Style Questions

`0 5` Compare how patriotism is presented in _next to of course god america i_ and **one** other poem from 'Conflict'.
(36 marks)

`0 6` Compare how individual experiences are explored in _Bayonet Charge_ and **one** other poem from 'Conflict'.
(36 marks)

Death

Q1   Link the descriptions of death below with the poem they come from.

> Which now all withering lay   _The Charge of the Light Brigade_
>
> While horse and hero fell   _Mametz Wood_
>
> My manners are tearing off heads   _next to of course god america i_
>
> heroic happy dead   _The Falling Leaves_
>
> their skeletons paused mid dance-macabre   _Hawk Roosting_

Q2   Choose four poems from the 'Conflict' cluster. Choose the term from the box that you think best summarises each poem's attitude to death. Give reasons to support your answers.

loss	grief
fate	pointlessness of life
pain and suffering	bravery
sacrifice	fate

Q3   Which of the poems you have studied do you think has the most positive view of death? Why?

Q4   Which of the poems you have studied do you think has the most negative view of death? Why?

Q5   For the poem you chose for either Q3 or Q4, explain how the poet uses poetic techniques in order to convey his or her views about death.

Helplessness

Q1 Think about situations when people experience helplessness.

Pete's friends were helpless when it came to convincing him that the Picasso shorts were a bad idea.

  a) Who or what can cause feelings of helplessness?

  b) How can feelings of helplessness be overcome?

  c) Are there any benefits to helplessness?

Q2 Choose a poem from the Conflict cluster.

  a) In what way is the main character helpless?

  b) How does the main character react to this helplessness?

Q3 Look at the poem you chose for Q2. How does the poet use form and structure to reinforce the sense of helplessness?

Q4 For each of the themes below, choose one poem from the Conflict cluster that deals with the theme, and explain how the theme is represented.

  a) physical barriers

  b) being controlled by others

  c) inability to escape

Exam-Style Questions

0 5 Compare how *Futility* and **one** other poem from 'Conflict' deal with the theme of death.

(36 marks)

0 6 Compare how feelings of helplessness are presented in *Out of the Blue* and **one** other poem from 'Conflict'.

(36 marks)

Mark Scheme

This section is a bit <u>different</u> — it's your chance to get inside the <u>examiner's mind</u>.

1) The mark scheme below is <u>very similar</u> to the one that the <u>examiners will use</u> to mark your actual exam answers.

2) The point of this section is to show you exactly what the examiners are <u>looking for</u> and <u>what you'll need to do</u> on the day to get high marks.

3) You have to <u>read</u> the <u>sample extracts</u> of exam answers. Then you'll either mark the answer and say how it can be improved, or add some extra points to make the answer better. The mark scheme will help you do this.

4) Before you start grading the sample answers, make sure you've read the mark scheme really <u>thoroughly</u> and that you <u>understand everything</u>.

Grade	What you've written
A*	• Explores several interpretations or meanings in detail • Provides carefully chosen and well-integrated quotes to back up ideas • Compares the poems thoughtfully and in detail, using plenty of evidence • Looks closely at <u>how</u> language, form and structure affect the reader, with well-chosen examples • Gives detailed and imaginative ideas about themes, attitudes and feelings • Considers the evidence to come up with conclusions about the poem
A	• Gives several interpretations or meanings • Provides well-chosen quotes to support ideas • Compares the poems in detail and provides plenty of evidence • Describes <u>how</u> language, form and structure affect the reader, using examples • Looks at themes, attitudes and feelings in detail, again using plenty of evidence
B	• Thoughtful interpretation of the poems • Supports interpretations with quotes from the text • Provides some well-chosen evidence to support comparisons between the poems • Gives several examples of <u>how</u> language, form and structure affect the reader • Provides some evidence to support ideas about themes, attitudes and feelings
C	• Comments on several aspects of the poem, e.g. mood, language, feelings, and uses quotes to back the comments up • Makes several comparisons between the poems • Explains <u>how</u> language, form and structure affect the reader • Makes valid comments about themes, attitudes or feelings in the poems

You'll also be marked on your <u>spelling</u>, <u>punctuation</u> and <u>grammar</u> and on how you <u>present</u> your work. To get the <u>best marks</u>, your essay should be <u>clearly organised</u> into <u>well-structured</u> paragraphs. It should also be <u>easy</u> to follow and <u>understand</u>.

Adding Quotes and Developing Points

The sample answers on this page have just one thing missing. Your task is to improve each point by adding a quote from the poem which backs it up. Good luck...

| 0 | 1 | Compare how ideas about patriotism are presented in *next to of course god america i* and one other poem from 'Conflict'. (36 marks) |

Answer Extract 1

In this sample answer, some sentences have letters like this: **(A)**.
Replace each letter with a suitable quote to help the student get a better grade.

> In 'next to of course god america i' and 'Flag', the poets explore their feelings about patriotism and the conflict that sometimes arises from it.
> Cummings' poem criticises the idea that it is right to be patriotic by using clichés, for example **(A)**, to show that the person speaking has a ridiculous point of view. Garbled sentences and over-the-top American slang, such as **(B)**, are also used to make the speaker sound foolish and comical. Agard is also critical of patriotism in his poem, specifically the idea that you might fight or even die in a war just to honour your flag. Repetition of the phrase **(C)** shows how foolish he believes this is.

Answer Extract 2

In this sample answer, some sentences have letters like this: **(A)**.
Replace each letter with a suitable quote to help the student get a better grade.

> Agard often uses quite mundane, ordinary language to talk about the flag in his poem. He uses simple, informal questions, such as **(A)** to directly involve the reader in his argument and to undermine the flag's power, stripping it of its noble connotations. Cummings, on the other hand, uses exaggerated language, such as **(B)**, to show how foolish he believes patriotism to be. This hyperbole makes the poem sound like the sort of speech that might be given to inspire soldiers before a battle, but Cummings is actually using it for the opposite purpose — to talk people out of conflict.

Adding Quotes and Developing Points

Two more extracts and two more tasks on this page — develop the points and finish the plan.

| 0 1 | Compare how ideas about patriotism are presented in *next to of course god america i* and one other poem from 'Conflict'. (36 marks) |

Answer Extract 3

In this sample answer, some sentences have letters like this: **(A)**. These points need to be developed further. Write an extra sentence to develop each point.

> Ideas about patriotism are challenged in both 'next to of course god america i' and 'Flag'. In both cases, the poets refuse to accept the traditional view that it is right and fitting to die for your country and instead portray conflict as a senseless and terrible thing.
>
> Both poets uses negative language to describe conflict. Cummings' speaker, for example, talks about "lions to the roaring slaughter". **(A).** Agard portrays conflict in a similar way when he says that the flag will "outlive the blood you bleed". This impresses on the reader just how misplaced most patriotism is. **(B)**

| 0 2 | Compare how ideas about conflict are presented in *Poppies* and one other poem from 'Conflict'. *(36 marks)* |

Sample Plan

The table below is a plan for an answer to the question above.

Find a quotation from the poem to back up each of the <u>language</u> points in the table. Make brief notes on your <u>personal response</u> to each poem to complete the plan.

	Poppies	**Futility**
Themes and ideas	A mother's feelings about war — someone indirectly involved	A soldier's feelings about war — it's a waste of life
Language	Emotive language ... **(A)** Metaphors ... **(B)**	Personification ... **(C)** Rhetorical questions ... **(D)**
Form and Structure	Absence of rhyme and rhythm makes it seem real and honest	Half rhyme seems informal and conversational
Personal Response	**(E)**	**(F)**

Marking Answer Extracts

This page is all about marking sample exam answers. If you're reading this without having read the mark scheme on p.44 first — do not collect £200 and certainly DO NOT pass GO.

| 0 | 3 | Compare how feelings about conflict are presented in *The Charge of the Light Brigade* and one other poem from 'Conflict'. *(36 marks)* |

Answer Extract 4

1) Use the mark scheme to <u>mark</u> this extract.
2) <u>Explain</u> how you decided on the grade and say how the answer could be <u>improved</u>.

> Both 'The Charge of the Light Brigade' and 'Bayonet Charge' are poems about the dangers of conflict outweighing the fact that people go to war in the name of their king and country.
>
> Tennyson's poem shows the bravery of the soldiers as they ride "into the valley of Death", with "Cannon to right of them, / Cannon to left of them, / Cannon in front of them". This repetition emphasises that there was no escape from the enemy, making the reader understand how terrifying the experience must have been. In 'Bayonet Charge', the poet describes how the person in the poem hears "Bullets smacking the belly out of the air"; this image really emphasises the horror and violence of war. Other words in the poem which add to the overall sense of fear are "shot-slashed" and "blue crackling air", both of which help to build up an image of something terrible.

This first extract has been <u>marked for you</u> to show you what to do.

Response: This answer gets a grade ⬚ B ⬚ because it talks about the themes of the poems and how the language affects the reader. It also provides examples of these things. To get a grade A it needs to develop points more fully and make closer comparisons between the poems.

Answer Extract 5

1) Use the mark scheme to <u>mark</u> this extract from a sample answer to the question above.
2) <u>Explain</u> how you decided on the grade and say how the answer could be <u>improved</u>.

> 'The Charge of the Light Brigade' is about a famous battle in the Crimean War, while 'Bayonet Charge' seems to be about conflict as a whole. In 'The Charge of the Light Brigade', the poet describes the battle that took place with phrases such as "Storm'd at with shot and shell, / Boldly they rode and well". He also seems to be praising the bravery of the soldiers who are facing "the jaws of Death" in the name of their king and country. In 'Bayonet Charge' the poet describes "The patriotic tear that had brimmed in his eye", which shows that this soldier is fighting for his country too. Both poems give a sense that war is difficult and frightening with descriptions of people being "shatter'd and sunder'd" in the first poem, and "dazzled with rifle fire" in the second. In both of these poems, the reader can clearly see that war is a terrible thing.

Marking Answer Extracts

Here's the exam question again and an extract from a sample answer to it.

| 0 3 | Compare how feelings about conflict are presented in *The Charge of the Light Brigade* and one other poem from 'Conflict'. *(36 marks)* |

Answer Extract 6

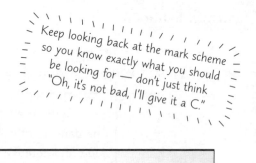

Keep looking back at the mark scheme so you know exactly what you should be looking for — don't just think "Oh, it's not bad, I'll give it a C."

1) Use the mark scheme on p.44 to <u>mark</u> this extract.

2) <u>Explain</u> how you decided on the grade and say how the answer could be <u>improved</u>.

> Tennyson describes how the soldiers were doomed to fail from the outset of the battle as he describes the "valley of Death". As the poem continues, each stanza shows events getting progressively worse for the cavalry — "they rode back, but not / not the six hundred". By the end of the poem, it is clear that the poet wants the reader to remember the events of the battle and to "Honour the Light Brigade". Hughes, in a similar way to Tennyson, places the reader in the middle of the battle and describes the scene vividly. We get a similar sense of how helpless the soldier in this poem is when the poet describes how he "lugged a rifle numb as a smashed arm" whilst "dazzled with rifle fire". Like in Tennyson's poem, there is a sense that the soldier may be doomed.
>
> Both poets describe people fighting for their monarch and their country; something that people tend to think of as the right thing to do. In 'Bayonet Charge', the poet describes "The patriotic tear that had brimmed in his eye", which makes it very clear that this is something the soldier is doing out of a sense of duty. In 'The Charge of the Light Brigade', the poet describes how the Brigade are fighting "Cossack and Russian" which makes it clear that they are fighting for their country. In both poems, this is shown to be a brave thing to do by the way in which the soldiers behave in the battle. In 'The Charge of the Light Brigade', they are "Storm'd at with shot and shell" and are described as riding into "the jaws of Death, / Into the mouth of Hell" whilst in 'Bayonet Charge' we hear that the soldier "plunged past with his bayonet", suggesting that he is totally focussed on his job, which is to kill the enemy.

Marking Answer Extracts

Different question, different sample answer. Hopefully you're getting into the examiner's mind-set by now...

> **0 2** Compare how ideas about conflict are presented in *Poppies* and one other poem from 'Conflict'.
>
> *(36 marks)*

Answer Extract 7

1) Use the mark scheme on p.44 to <u>mark</u> this extract.

2) <u>Explain</u> how you decided on the grade and say how the answer could be <u>improved</u>.

Don't forget to keep looking back at the mark scheme.

> Both 'Poppies' and 'Futility' present ideas about the impact that conflict has on people, although from different points of view. In the first poem, we are presented with a mother's concern for her son as he goes to war; in the second poem, the impact that war has already had on a person is explored.
>
> In both poems, emotive language is used to sum up the feelings that the poets have about conflict. Owen begins with the title 'Futility' which immediately suggests that this is what he thinks of war — that it is something which is ultimately pointless. He goes on to support this idea through the rest of the poem. Weir uses the title 'Poppies', now a universal symbol for the war dead, which again sets the negative tone for the poem. As the poem continues, Weir's narrator describes how she "was brave", and how her "stomach [was] busy / making tucks, darts, pleats", both of which suggest that she is struggling to hold in her fear over what might happen to her soldier son. Owen's narrator, on the other hand, does not try to conceal his feelings — it is clear that he is upset about what happened during the war.

Efforts to persuade Jim he'd gone out in his underwear were an exercise in futility.

Marking a Complete Answer

New page, new question and answer. Only this time it's the whole answer, not just an extract...

| 0 4 | Compare how divisions in society are presented in *At The Border, 1979* and one other poem from 'Conflict'. | *(36 marks)* |

Answer 8

Make sure you've <u>read</u> the <u>advice</u> and <u>mark</u> <u>scheme</u> on page 44.

Read the <u>whole</u> answer. Use the mark scheme to <u>mark</u> the answer.
<u>Explain</u> how you decided on the grade and say how the answer could be <u>improved</u>.

'The Right Word' and 'At the Border, 1979' both present ideas about divisions in society which can result in conflict, in ways which seem very real and believable.

Dharker makes use of negative language which is often used in the media, such as "terrorist" and "hostile militant". These kinds of words tend to make people think the worst of those being described, increasing division and therefore conflict. Throughout the poem, she explores ideas about 'The Right Word' and the fact that the words we use can have a wider impact than we might think — the "guerrilla warrior" actually "is a child who looks like mine". This may make the reader think twice about how they judge people who have been labelled in this way. Hardi also presents the idea that people's attitudes cause divisions in 'At the Border, 1979'. Although the mother in this poem says that the "landscape is more beautiful" and "people are much kinder" in her own country, the young child can't see any real difference between the place they are in and the place they are going to. This suggests that our prejudices against other nations are often unfounded.

In both cases, the poems are written in the first person which makes them feel very immediate and real. In 'At the Border, 1979' this is enhanced by the use of clear, simple descriptions, which give the reader a clear sense of the place and the emotions that are present in the different characters. We can see from this poem that people's emotions are important, and this helps us to understand that divisions in society are often more about emotion than about physical divisions. The same is true of 'The Right Word', which has a sense of immediacy partly as a result of the use of "I" and partly because of the sense that the events in the poems are happening now. In this case, the divisions in society are again emotional — it is what people think about other people that causes conflict and fear.

Marking a Complete Answer

This is the second half of the answer on p.50.

Dharker uses the structure of her poem to show how little people often understand other people. The first seven stanzas all give stereotypical views of the person "in the shadows". He or she is a "terrorist" who is "lurking" but eventually turns out to be a "child". This suggests that if people take the time to think about their stereotyped views, they might come to a better understanding. It might also imply, though, that people's negative views are so deep-rooted that it takes a lot of time and effort to change them. Similarly, Hardi uses fragmented stanzas to suggest that her poem is a real memory. We see things incompletely and in an unstructured fashion, making the poem seem more believable.

Dharker's message that conflict is a result of confusion and misunderstanding is a believable one because most readers will have heard some of the negative terms at some point. However, she is not solely negative; in the final two stanzas, she shows that her view of the person "outside the door" has changed and that it is possible to accept people and ideas that we don't understand if we make the effort to "open the door". This gives the reader a strong sense of hope for the future because it shows that it is possible to accept people who are different and to avoid conflict. Hardi takes a similar view that it is possible to move past differences and to cross boundaries. She describes how the "chain was removed" which could mean mental barriers as well as physical ones. Again, I think that this makes the poem hopeful because it shows that people can change. This feeling is enhanced when she writes that "the same chain of mountains encompassed all of us", which links with Dharker's idea that the child is "like your son, too" — we are all the same once we strip away our prejudices.

Overall, I think that both poems show that divisions in society come from people's prejudices, and can be avoided if we look at the world with open eyes rather than listening to what "My mother informed me" (Hardi) or the words that other people use. Dharker says that "No words can help me now" which suggests that it is often words that cause conflict and that we should act "carefully" in order to avoid it.

__*Acknowledgements*__

The Publisher would like to thank:

John Agard: 'Flag' — From *Half Caste and Other Poems* by John Agard, first published in the UK by Hodder Children's, an imprint of Hachette Children's Books, 338 Euston Road, London, NW1 3BH
Simon Armitage: Extract from *Out of the Blue* — Enitharmon, 2008, reproduced by permission of Enitharmon
Ciaran Carson: 'Belfast Confetti' — By kind permission of the author and The Gallery Press, Loughcrew, Oldcastle, County Meath, Ireland from Collected Poems (2008)
E.E. Cummings: 'next to of course god america i' is reprinted from *COMPLETE POEMS 1904-1962*, by E.E. Cummings, edited by George J. Firmage, by permission of W.W. Norton & Company. Copyright © 1991 by the Trustees for the E.E. Cummings Trust and George James Firmage.
Imtiaz Dharker: 'The Right Word' — Imtiaz Dharker, *The Terrorist at my Table* (Bloodaxe Books, 2006)
Choman Hardi: 'At the Border, 1979' — Choman Hardi, *Life for Us* (Bloodaxe Books, 2004)
Ted Hughes: 'Bayonet Charge' — From *The Hawk in the Rain*, 9780571086146, Faber and Faber, first published 1957
Ted Hughes: 'Hawk Roosting' — From Lupercal Faber and Faber; Reprint of 1970 edition (8 Oct 1985) ISBN-13: 978-0571092468
Robert Minhinnick: 'The Yellow Palm' — from *King Driftwood* (Carcanet Press, 2008) reproduced by permission of Carcanet Press Ltd
Margaret Postgate Cole: 'The Falling Leaves' — From *Scars Upon My Heart* selected by Catherine Reilly (Virago, 1981), reproduced by permission of David Higham Associates
Owen Sheers: 'Mametz Wood' — Copyright © 2005 Owen Sheers. Reproduced by permission of the author c/o Rogers, Coleridge & White Ltd., 20 Powis Mews, London W11 1JN
Stevie Smith: 'Come On, Come Back' — Estate of James MacGibbon
Jane Weir: 'Poppies' — By kind permission of Templar Poetry on behalf of the author, 2009

Every effort has been made to locate copyright holders and obtain permission to reproduce poems and images. For those poems and images where it has been difficult to trace the originator of the work, we would be grateful for information. If any copyright holder would like us to make an amendment to the acknowledgements, please notify us and we will gladly update the book at the next reprint. Thank you.